Three Wishes

Three Wishes

PHILIP TERRY

Patrician Press ● Manningtree

Philip Terry is currently Director of the Centre for Creative Writing at the University of Essex. Among his books are the lipogrammatic novel *The Book of Bachelors*, the edited story collection *Ovid Metamorphosed*, a translation of Raymond Queneau's last book of poems *Elementary Morality*, and the poetry volumes *Oulipoems*, *Oulipoems 2*, *Shakespeare's Sonnets*, and *Advanced Immorality*. His novel *tapestry* was shortlisted for the 2013 Goldsmith's Prize. A new poetry collection, *Dante's Inferno,* which relocates Dante's action to current day Essex, is forthcoming from Carcanet.

Published by Patrician Press 2014.
For more information: www.patricianpress.com

First published as a paperback edition by Patrician Press 2014
E-book edition published by Patrician Press 2014

British Library Cataloguing in Publication Data. A catalogue record for this book is available from the British Library.

ISBN 978-0-9927235-7-6

Printed and bound in Peterborough by Printondemand-worldwide

www.patricianpress.com

Acknowledgements

Thanks to the editors of *Artefiction: Notes from the Post Punk Underground* (Stride) and *PN Review,* where earlier versions of "A Punk Diary" and "A Brief Anthology of Jazz" first appeared.

A BRIEF ANTHOLOGY OF JAZZ

CLEO BROWN

In May 1922 in Weimar, the Bauhaus stage a production of Shakespeare's *A Midsummer Night's Dream*. Kandinsky plays Theseus to his wife's Hippolyta, while Paul Klee and his wife take the roles of their fairy counterparts.

DON BYAS

A fable sometimes ascribed to Aesop, but most likely of later authorship, tells the story of a horse and an ass travelling to market with their master. Both carry heavy bags and after a while the horse begins to tire, so the donkey offers to carry his burden. After some time the master sees the horse, now trotting along gaily, and upbraids it for its idleness: as punishment the horse is made to carry both bags. The donkey, who had calculated that things would turn out in just this manner, travels the rest of the journey load-free. It is the ass's cunning here, which most clearly suggests inauthenticity, for in Aesop this is characteristic of the fox, the ass being noted for its stupidity. Various morals have been appended to the story, such as "Never trust a favour which comes from an evil-doer", "You never get something for nothing" and "An honest face may hide a cunning heart". Sometimes these are used as titles, though more often the piece is simply called:

MILES DAVIS

When Pierre Levallois called out the Gas Board they could find absolutely nothing wrong with his cooker. To their surprise, however, Mr. Levallois still insisted on having it replaced. Asked for an explanation, Pierre stated his grievance:

DUKE ELLINGTON

A hit man who made a point of only operating out of town, wondered if this was common practice in his profession. Happening to meet a colleague for lunch, he took the opportunity to set his mind at rest, asking straight up:

HERSCHEL EVANS

When archaeologists working in deep waters off the northern coast of Crete discover the ancient and barnacle encrusted shell of a giant clam, on which are found traces of human DNA, it is thought that they have perhaps found the shell that gave birth to Venus, long thought to have been purely mythological. On hearing the news, Belgian anthropologist Marcel Gallet exclaims:

WALLY FAWKES

In hell, Paisley meets up with some of his most admired heroes, notably King William of Orange, who kindly offers to be his guide. Seeing the devil approaching, brandishing a red hot triton, the anxious Paisley turns to his guide, and asks:

DAVE FRISHBERG

After years of living in the shadow of James Galway, Irish composer James McMahon, disciple of Schoenberg and his pupils, finally finds recognition after his critical success at the Connaught Contemporary Music Festival. Not only does he sweep the board where prizes are concerned, the panel of judges recommend that a new national holiday should be inaugurated in his name.

FRANKIE FROEBA

At a wedding reception the hotel manager loses his monogrammed silk handkerchief, which for years he has worn in his breast pocket, regarding it as something of a talisman. When the groom recovers it, caught in the branches of a juniper tree in the garden, the manager is so delighted that he offers to cover the bar costs out of his own pocket.

JESSE FULLER

Two harlots see Simon Stylites on his pillar. One of them approaches nearer, exchanges a few words with him, then returns to her companion, who asks bluntly:

ERROL GARNER

When Ruth Rendell was introduced to him at the Royal Garden Party, the latest recipient of the Royal Garter for Jazz, she was at once convinced that she had met him before, though certainly in some other capacity. Later, much later, it suddenly struck her who in fact he was:

DIZZY GILLESPIE

A fish disguised as a man went to the dentist's out of curiosity. As soon as he opened his mouth the dentist looked puzzled, asking his assistant to come and take a look at once. Only one thought filled the mind of the anxious fish:

JOHNNY GRIFFIN

A housewife complains to her friend about the irregularity of her sexual congress with husband John, who is always out on the town while she labours at home caring for their two children. She qualifies her complaint adding that they still enjoy loud and enthusiastic congress on those rare occasions when he stays in.

CORKY HALE

Having lined his study with cork, Proust found the chief source of disturbance to be the noises which continued to insinuate themselves into this room via the one remaining aperture in his door. There was, he reflected, only one solution:

ADELAIDE HALL

Not quite sure of the words, but remembering the tune and the general drift, a father responds to his son's request for a rendition of "Aiken Drum", singing:

> And he played upon a banjo
> A banjo, a banjo
> And he played upon a banjo
> And his name was Aiken Drum!

Spotting his mistake at once, the child starts to cry, then shouts at the top of his voice:

WYNONIE HARRIS

A 1604 production of *Hamlet*, performed by touring players in Exeter, had to be abandoned during Act III Scene 4, when Hamlet, rather than Polonius, collapsed on the floor, apparently lifeless. Hours later, when the cast eventually succeeded in resuscitating the unfortunate actor, he explained that on thrusting his sword through the arras so as to kill Polonius, he had become giddy with terror on perceiving a large red stain, at the exact point where his sword had struck. Rushing to inspect the arras, and verify the truth of his claim, the actors were amused to discover what was almost certainly a wine stain, which the stagehands had failed to remove following the previous night's cast party.

COLEMAN HAWKINS

With masterful economy, an ex-miner-turned-artist sculpts his female nudes from the very mineral he once laboured to extract from the earth.

NEAL HEFTI

The reasons given by Councillor Jock McMenemy for refusing to give cousin Brian Stewart free access to the Labour Hall on the occasion of his silver wedding anniversary were as logical as they were succinct:

TONY KINSEY

Asked the secret of his success, a blind jazz musician explains that while his sight may be impaired, he can nevertheless visualise the slightest modulations in sound, and project these, not onto his retina, but straight into his trombone.

LEE KONITZ

After chucking him out once and for all, she turned her thoughts to revenge. Then, having carefully considered her options, she spread his collection of jazz classics over the carpet, squatted, and began to piss.

SHELLEY MANNE

The escutcheon of an Amazon tank commander depicts the head of a blonde muscle man, broken in two like an egg, above a pool of blood. Beneath it, an inscription reads:

MIKE MANTLER

A percussionist, who ran a sideline in taxidermy, was fired with enthusiasm when a friend presented him with a contact microphone on his thirtieth birthday. At once he saw the revolutionary potential of this gadget, and charged about his house like a madman, miking and percussing an array of everyday objects - chairs, tables, toilet seats, sofas, bins, radiators - liberating their sonorous potential which till now had lain unperceived and dormant. At last, in a frenzy of excitement, he pointed to his prize stag's head mounted on the wall, and cried importunately to his companion:

GERRY MULLIGAN

The Somme, Christmas Day 1917, 9.00 am. Not a single shot has been fired since dawn, singing issues from the German trenches, and the smell of warm wine and cloves drifts over no-man's-land.

SONNY ROLLINS

A father of conservative persuasion, who ruled his family with a rod of iron, was dumbstruck when he encountered his eldest son in the street with a pierced ear. Later, when he regained his powers of speech, he was found in the bathroom, yelling:

TONY SCOTT

Ever since the day of his birth it had been clear to his parents that he was in no way a normal child. The birth, indeed, had been traumatic for all concerned: first a hand had popped out, then fallen on the floor with a sickening plop, the rest of the infant remaining in the womb for several more hours. Then, bit by bloodied bit, the rest of the child started to emerge: a severed head, a leg, then another leg, a torso, mercifully attached to two arms, then the final hand, followed at last by the afterbirth. The doctors stitched the child together as best they could, and proclaimed it nothing short of a miracle when the boy survived the operation. And then, for a year or so, things had settled down, the child behaving to all accounts more or less normally. Then, one day, out of the blue, things began to go wrong again: having brought the infant downstairs for breakfast, his mother went to change his bed. What she saw left her terror-stricken: beneath the blanket, nestled in the corner among his bears and other soft toys, lay a pink and perfectly formed big toe.

PHIL SEAMAN

He had known Beth for a long time, had once had a crush on her even, though he had never met her long-standing partner Ruth. But perhaps this was for the best. At first, when Beth had phoned him, then met him in a bar, ablaze with news and smoking like a trooper, he had thought she was going to say they were splitting up, and for a moment he saw his old passion being rekindled. Yet he couldn't have been further from the truth: they wanted to have a baby. And, what's more, they wanted him to be the sperm donor. He was certainly taken aback, and at once ordered another drink, but in the end, despite reservations, he agreed. Three weeks later, at the designated time, he turned up on cue, already hard with expectation at the thought of Beth awaiting him. Then Ruth appeared, wearing a lab coat and surgical gloves, wielding a turkey-baster. Handing him the test tube, she demanded coldly that he deposit his sperm therein.

REX STEWART

Completely out of their heads and confronted by an empty larder two hungry art critics are reduced to tearing still lives off the wall, one by Paul Klee, "Around the Fish", one by Filippo de Pisis, "Marine Still Life with Lobster and Feathers", which they proceed to cut up, place in a casserole, and simmer over a low flame.

WILBUR SWEATMAN

On the occasion of his marriage to Mad Meg a Dorset Chapter biker arranged his honeymoon at Burgh Island. When he turned up drunk with forty-five choppers in tow he was promptly shown the door. Irate that he had left his shotgun at home, he rode off into the night, already planning to return the following day with fully armed reinforcements, to enact his dreadful revenge.

SOPHIE TUCKER

Before taking the train to Glastonbury, a girl leaves her father strict instructions: the UCCA form is to be put in the post, the cheque from Esso in the building society. The following day, her father completely forgets what his daughter has told him, and absent-mindedly posts the cheque along with the form.

JOE VENUTI

In the cafés which cover the slopes of Mount Olympus there still lingers a belief in the pagan gods which once openly frolicked in the surrounding olive groves. There, they still maintain that Jove, not the Christian Jehovah, is omnipresent. An American tourist, unaware that he might be in danger of risking blasphemy, asked the café owner if Jove, therefore, was in his cup of tea? The proprietor, unperturbed, answered forthrightly: of course!

GROVER WASHINGTON

Having expressed his disdain for the country life, the town mouse asks his rural cousin if he can use the bathroom, if indeed there is one, to freshen up before his return. Insulted by his cousin's behaviour, the country mouse refuses him the use of his toilet, saying that if he is so happy with life in the town he would surely be better off performing his ablutions there.

MARY LOU WILLIAMS

At the Country Fair the mayor is most impressed by the "Igloo", a dome-shaped family tent of advanced design which folds up into the size of a football, while his deputy, Will Butler, is taken by the locally grown giant yams.

LESTER YOUNG

When Freud and Jung split over Freud's insistence on the pervasiveness of sexuality in the workings of psychoneuroses, the psychoanalytic movement was itself deeply divided; yet in the end, for better of worse, the majority chose to follow Freud, while only a few flocked to the defence of his colleague.

KEY

Klee Auberon

"Done by Ass"

My ol' stove hiss!

Do you kill in town?

Her shell! Heavens!

Wull ee fork us?

Day for Irish Berg

For hanky free bar

Did you see if he'll err?

Her old gardener

Does he gill espy?

John eager if in

Cork keyhole

Had a ladle!

Wine on the arras

Coal mannequins

Nay a lefty

Tone he can see

Leak on hits

Shell he-man

Mike my antler!

Jerry mull again

Son! Ear! Hole in his!

Toe in his cot

Fill! Semen!

Wrecks stew art

Will Burgh sweat man!

Esso fee to UCCA

Jove in your tea

Get over! Wash in town!

Mayor "Igloo", Will yams

Less to Jung

A LITTLE ILLUSTRATED ABC

BA-BE-BI-BO-BU

Possessed of a rebellious distaste for the colour pink, the young girl throws a fit when her parents present her with a Barbie doll on her fifth birthday. Industriously, her mother knocks up an outfit in blue denim, and in this get-up Barbie comes slowly to find favour. Wishing to restore a degree of femininity to Barbie, the mother hits on the strategy of adding a blue bow, tied round the neck. Picking up the car keys, she heads into town, only one thing on her mind:
Barbie: buy bow (blue).

CA-CE-CI-CO-CU

Because these men were united by a common goal, namely to kick their cocaine habits, because they favoured outdoor sports, especially sailing, as a means to this end, because, too, of their tendency to dress in Safari, they soon came to be referred to

collectively, by themselves as well as others, as the KKCC:
Khaki Kick Coke Crew.

DA-DE-DI-DO-DU

Though everybody called her Do she thought of herself as Doreen, perhaps because here she heard an echo of her late mother's name, Irene, perhaps too because the name was hated by her father. He it was, Doreen was sure of it, who had hounded her mother into an early grave, gradually wearing down her spirit until there was no longer any will to live; Doreen's revenge, in contrast, was to be much more sudden. That night, as her father slept, she plunged the carving knife into his breast, alarming the neighbours who heard the following frenzied exchange:

— Daddy! Die!

— Do!

— Do!

FA-FE-FI-FO-FU

When the adventure is all over - the trip to market, the bean, the argument with his mother, the beanstalk, the land of the giant, the golden eggs, the chase, the descent, the cutting of the beanstalk with the axe - Jack finally collapses on the grass in exhaustion. Far off, he hears the fading and now idle threat of the giant as he plunges to his death. Afar: Fe, fi, fo, fu———

GA-GE-GI-GO-GU

As Hen Nights go, the evening had started soberly enough, with gin and tonics at a local wine bar. Later, things were to get more out of hand. After three more bars and a light meal, the Hens ended up at a male strip club. Naked men poured out of every doorway, charging about like wild animals. The bride-to-be was presented with a dog collar and a lead, and a leather gag to tie over the mouth of her chosen he-man. As she tottered onto the parquet, barely able to distinguish one sweating torso from the next, her delirious companions cheered her on from the touchlines.

Gag a guy! Go! Goooooo!

HA-HE-HI-HO-HU

A Japanese businessman, known to his friends as Joju, recently recruited by the KKCC, is shown some educational videos at his first meeting. In one of them he is surprised to see his boss totally off his face at a party and, unsure how he is meant to react, finds himself stifling a laugh.

Hah! He high! Hohu!

JA-JE-JI-JO-JU

After his first month in the KKCC, having touched no drugs during this period, Joju's powers of resistance are put to the test. One of the crew takes down a large jar of cocaine, prominently marked with the letter "G"

(denoting its country of origin), and places it before him. Help yourself, he says. Stoically, Joju resists.
Jar "G": yer high Joju.

KA-KE-KI-KO-KU

As a reward for his success during the one-month trial period, Joju is presented with a KKCC car key, and invited to drive one of the crew Land Rovers on a weekend excursion to the Pennines.
Car key (Kick Coke Crew).

LA-LE-LI-LO-LU

After the Great Irish Theme Pub Robbery, St. Patrick's Day 1998, media coverage was so intense that the ringleaders quickly became household names: McGuiness, McCaffery, Smith, O'Neill, Fisher, Lawley. The plan, unexpectedly leaked to the police, had been to make for France via Newhaven, but as everyone now knows this was not to be:

McGuiness, McCaffery, Smith and Fisher were arrested before they left British soil. O'Neill and Lawley, it was widely supposed, had gone to ground, and all the police could do was wait. Their patience was rewarded in the first days of April, and arrest quickly followed, when they intercepted a telegram sent from Halifax, reading:

Lawley: lie low Looe.

MA-ME-MI-MO-MU

Before going to bed, as a special treat, the child persuades his mother to play a game: she is to imitate a farm animal, without speaking or otherwise uttering a sound, and he is to guess what the beast is. The mother gets down on all fours and proceeds to chew the carpet. At first the child is puzzled, then, in a sudden flash, he sees what his mother is up to: *chewing the grass, like a...cow!*

Mammy! Mime! Oh! Moo!

NA-NE-NI-NO-NU

Given half a chance, the children liked nothing better than to play at Teletubbies, preferably accompanied by the Dyson, Noo-noo. Yet they could only do so when Nanny was asleep, for she was under strict instructions to keep them away from all electrical appliances. While they played, then, they had to be vigilant at all times, and if ever Nanny was heard on the move, the alarm signal was given at once:

Nanny nigh: no Noo!

PA-PE-PI-PO-PU

At the height of the Teletubbies craze, a father finds himself tyrannized by his son in the bathroom. The son, affectionately nicknamed "Pie" prior to this late flourishing of the anal phase, now dressed as Teletubbies' Po, squats purposefully on his potty to empty his bowels, ordering his father, meanwhile, to urinate.

Pa pee! Pie (Po) poo.

QUA-QUE-QUI-QUO-QU

At the court of Empress Sadako, Sei Shonagon finds herself irritated by the herb doctor Norimasa, whose boisterous energy and quack remedies have won him favour with her mistress, to such an extent that she neglects affairs of state. Wishing to undermine his ascendancy, she consults captain Wu, who suggests administering a soporific so that Norimasa will be unfit to attend the Empress. The following morning, delighted by the immediate success of the enterprise, Sei Shonagon sends her accomplice a note of congratulation:

Quack weak: quick work Wu.

RA-RE-RI-RO-RU

One day, Pooh bear wakes up to find one of his eyes missing. What is to be done? All the animals in the Hundred Acre Wood gather together: Kanga, Roo, Owl, Piglet, Rabbit, Eeyore, Tigger and the rest. After much

inconclusive debate, Owl speaks up with his customary authority: they must send an envoy to Rare Eye Row, in the town, for only there will they find what they are looking for. To decide who is to make the perilous journey, lots are drawn. The task falls to Roo, who sets off without complaint.
Rare Eye Row: Roo.

SA-SE-SI-SO-SU
A black labourer on a Texan farm reports disinterestedly his boss's crazy decision to take neighbour Simon Marshall to court, having seen him trespass on his land.
Sah see Si so sue.

TA-TE-TI-TO-TU
At the Yugoslavian premiere of *Mon Oncle* Jacques Tati and President Tito discuss film and theatre: despite differences of taste and politics they find themselves united in their

admiration for the work of British actor Peter O'Toole.

Tati, Tito: O'Toole.

VA-VE-VI-VO-VU

Embarking on their ill-fated tour of the USA, The Sex Pistols are met by hordes of photographers at Heathrow. Vicious tells them if they want a picture it'll cost them a fiver, otherwise he'll bust their cameras. Attempting to calm things down, Rotten intervenes, then, turning to Vicious, snarls:

Vey ave a viver f'you.

WA-WE-WI-WO-WU

Having spent the best part of his adult life studying the behavioural patterns of the Wahwee tribe of Borneo, the Belgian anthropologist Marcel Gallet could still not understand why the tribe persistently and systematically looked for trouble, an enigma

which he famously summarized in these words:
Wahwee: why woe woo?

XA-XE-XI-XO-XU

On the eve of revolution, Tzar Nicholas II goes on a trip to North America. He is taken on a visit to a Sioux reservation, where chiefs Running Dog and Sitting Bear, beneficiaries of the latest medical advances, proudly display their appendix scars.
Tzar sees sides of Sioux.

YA-YE-YI-YO-YU

London club owner, M___ , finding himself in a monetary dispute with the Krays, agreed to accept a dated IOU, which he subsequently carried on his person wherever he went. Cornered one night at gunpoint by one of the Kray gang, he was told to hand it back, no questions asked, or forfeit his life.
You or your IOU.

ZA-ZE-ZI-ZO-ZU

A Frenchman, living in a rented flat overlooking Regent's Park, complained to his landlord that he could not sleep at nights, it was no good, he would have to go. When pressed, he said it was the close proximity to London Zoo that disturbed him: at night, he felt oppressed by the mournful eyes of the animals which, he insisted, glared at him from the depths of their cages, burrowing their way into his troubled dreams.

Zere are zees eyes au zoo.

A PUNK DIARY

MONDAY

Met Hank in town for a few beers. Said he'd been told to cut down on peanuts by the doctor because of his acne. Chocolate, he said, was another danger, but no way was he giving up Star Bar.

TUESDAY

Checked out some local bands at The Essex: all crap. To make up for a bad night I tried to score some blow, but soon found out the only joy I was likely to get was from D_____ , who had already left.

SUNDAY

Went round Scottie's to make sure he didn't slit his wrists or do anything stupid after being dumped by his girlfriend. Needn't have bothered. Turned out he'd been losing interest any case.

TUESDAY

Hung out in Parrot Records for a couple of hours chatting to Nigel, listening to some new singles. Best offering of the week was *Rip off Yourself* by a spineless looking group called The Cons. Great chorus:

> You fuck up your mind
> You fuck up your health
> You're so fucked up
> You rip off yourself!

FRIDAY

Went to see The Murk at The 100 Club. Seriously underrated band. Must remember to get their new double A side *The Axe/Dents*.

MONDAY

Bumped into Scottie's ex in the High Street, barely recognised her with her new peroxide mohican. She asked me how Scottie was getting on and I lied, said he was still pining after her. We had a cup of tea in The Shanty and talked about old times. Told me she'd got a job with a ferry company, starting at the end of the month.

WEDNESDAY

Auditioned for local outfit Pheromones: crap. I didn't want them and they didn't want me, so I packed up my bass and walked home.

SATURDAY

Got off with O_____ after a local punk gig. Lick my decals, she said, so I did. Later, before crashing, we smoked a few spliffs. Left a bitter taste in my mouth as the hot pot smoke hit the decals on my tongue.

THURSDAY

Met Hank in town for a few beers. Told me about local five-piece The Lepers breaking down on their way to a gig in Amsterdam.

Apparently the transit they'd hired had a blowout and the spare tyre was punctured as well, so they missed the gig and any chance of making their mark on Europe. When they got back they'd given the manager at Hertz an earful.

TUESDAY

Spent the weekend at Henge: heavy festival. Mainly bikers and metal heads so bit out of it. Hank took three black stars and had a bad trip. Fell into a river, and when he emerged, caked in mud, announced in visionary tones: *Hell viscous, tell O_____.*

FRIDAY

Went round O_____'s for a chat and a smoke. Was just starting to feel horny when she farted, filling the room with the smell of old eggs.

MONDAY

Another audition for local band: usual crap. This lot, Automatic Hamsters, had a really awful song about Crufts, with the chorus:

> It's a machine where pets are done
> It's legal canine desecra—tion!

WEDNESDAY

Bumped into Scottie in town and went for a tea in The Shanty. Told him about his ex going to sea but he didn't seem that interested. Nearly ripped off by a couple of kids rummaging through our gear but Scottie spotted them just in time, told them to keep their hands in their ain coats.

SATURDAY

Went to see The Murk at The Lyceum. Great gig. Couple of tall skins had me worried on the way home though. They were more or less blocking the pavement but I knew if I turned and ran they'd have me, so I just kept on walking, so as not to put any ideas in their heads. As luck would have it they weren't in an aggressive mood, and let me pass, without a word.

MONDAY

Went into Parrot Records to check out the discs. Nigel played me the latest sounds, including an EP on vomit coloured vinyl by Repulsive Strings, and a dire song about a blind girl regaining her sight, "She'll See!", by a Dutch outfit.

TUESDAY

Bumped into Hamsters' singer Mitch in town. He's a nice bloke, even if he can't sing and writes crap lyrics. Went to sniff some glue in the multi-storey till chased out by an attendant, shouting madly, pointing at us.

THURSDAY

Met Hank in town for a few beers. Talked about celebrity spotting. I told him I'd seen Joe Strummer in the King's Road, which was a lie. He told me he'd seen Keith Levine in Texas Homecare.

MONDAY

Spent weekend at Reading. Got really out of it and missed most of the bands except Motorhead, who were crap. Punks and rockers at each other's throats. Hank had a bad trip on a red microdot and thought he was in Japan. He wouldn't snap out of it and for hours he just sat huddled in the corner of the tent, rabbiting on about something to do with Japanese currency.

THURSDAY

Went round O_____'s for a chat. Got a bit stoned and played I Spy. Totally confused when O_____ spies something beginning with "N" or "G". It had to be one or the other, I said, which made her cross, so I thought it best to go. I still don't know what she had in mind, but if she was thinking of "Gnome" it's definitely got a "G", I've checked.

SATURDAY

Went to see The Murk at Dingwall's. Great as always. They encored with their new song about youth culture, "These Kids", which is fast becoming an anthem for a new generation.

TUESDAY

Went to a local gig at The Essex: Pheromones plus support. Plus support turned out to be The Tools and Automatic Hamsters. Place was packed out largely because of new act Tools with Nigel from Parrot on bass. Crap in my opinion but the Essex manager loved them, paid them £50 *and* asked them back.

WEDNESDAY

Met Hank in town for a few beers. Apparently The Lepers had broken down *again*, this time on the way to Manchester. Again, Hertz were to blame.

FRIDAY

O_____'s birthday. Went round to see her with Hank, Scottie, Nigel and others. We played discs late into the night and got more and more wasted. We all did a mad dance to The Fall and collapsed in a heap on the floor.

KEY

Peanut ration

Penetration

Blow on D_____

Blondie

Gang off her

Gang of Four

The meek Cons

The Mekons

The Axe/Dents

The Accidents

Ex to sea

XTC

Pheromones

The Ramones

Decal ash

The Clash

The five berate Hertz

The Vibrators

Hell viscous, tell O_____

Elvis Costello

Eggy parp

Iggy Pop

It's law to ruin the dogs

Slaughter and the Dogs

Their ain coats

The Raincoats

Tall skinheads

Talking Heads

"She'll See!"

Chelsea

You two!

U2

Levine in Texas

Living in Texas

No yen...no yen...no yen...

999

Spies "N" or "G"

Spizz Energy

"These Kids"

The Skids

The Essex pays Tools

The Sex Pistols

They'll irk Hertz

The Lurkers

The floor

The Flaw

Note

Between 1970 and 1982, every January, almost without exception, Georges Perec sent his friends small pamphlets with his best wishes for the New Year. These were collections of short texts based on homophonic variations which Perec had printed in a run of 100 copies, and which he then signed and sent out to his friends. They were published posthumously, in book form, in 1989 under the title *Voeux* (*New Year's Greetings*), by Éditions du Seuil. The collection contains a dazzling assemblage of material with nods to musicology, crime fiction, Latin translations, works by Perec and his fellow Oulipians, and cinema. Each piece, in the manner of Raymond Roussel, begins with a series of homophonic plays-on-words, then proceeds to construct miniature narratives out of this material, the "method" often being explained in a key at the end of the text. The three pieces presented here are neither translations of this material (which is, by its very nature, untranslatable), nor entirely original pieces of work, rather a sort of homage to Perec: "A Brief Anthology of Jazz" and "A Little Illustrated ABC" take their inspiration directly from two of Perec's pieces ("Gamine de blouse" of 1979 and "Petit abécédaire illustré" of 1970); "A Punk Diary" responds more freely to Perec's material. There is no evidence I know of to suggest Perec was at all interested in punk rock, but as the material for *Voeux* is more often than not drawn from popular culture, and as the punk movement began during the period when Perec was writing these brief texts, it seemed appropriate as a starting point. The pieces have been collected together on the occasion of the New Year 2014, to celebrate the first year of Patricia Borlenghi's Patrician Press.

PT

BV - #0040 - 201223 - C0 - 216/138/3 - PB - 9780992723576 - Matt Lamination